Welcome

Hello Kitty's Neighborhood

BENDON

**Bendon Publishing
International**
Ashland, OH 44805

SIL-34055

Sanrio
© 1976, 2004 SANRIO CO., LTD.
Used Under License.
www.sanrio.com

Welcome to Hello Kitty's Neighborhood!

Hello Kitty's house has a red roof.

Hello Kitty loves to garden.

This is
Hello Kitty's bedroom.

Good Morning!

Can you find these words in this word search?

breakfast
cereal
eggs
kitchen
mama
milk
pancakes

e g g s o v p t w z
b r e a k f a s t k
c m o r n i n g m i
a e t q m h c q r t
q p r f a j a l m c
r k w e m q k d i h
y b n p a o e a l e
t a k z e l s q k n

Answers in the back.

**Hello Kitty enjoys breakfast
with Papa, Mama and Mimmy.**

Hello Kitty and Fifi wait for the school bus.

Help the bus driver find his way to the school!

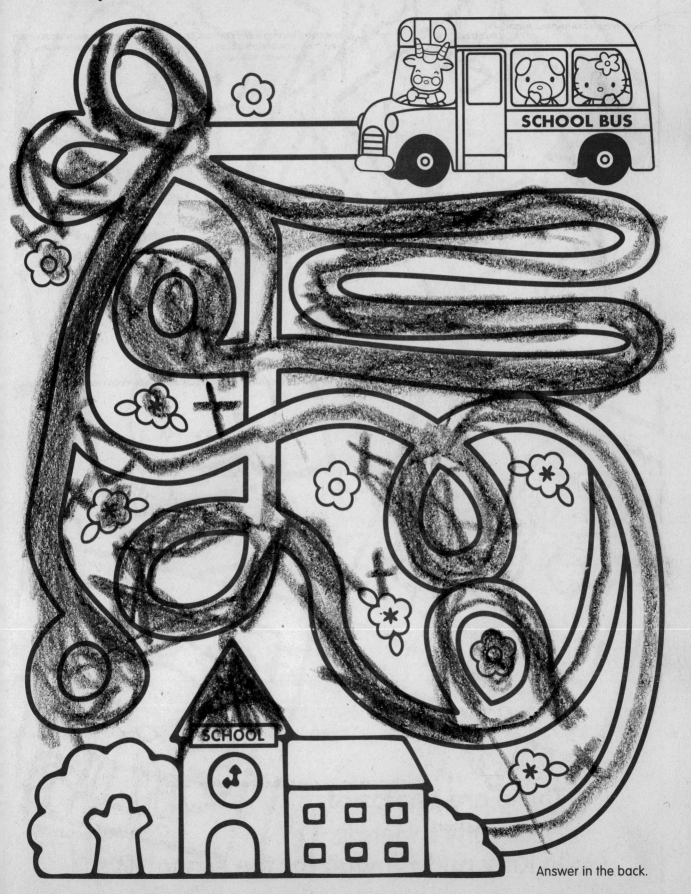

SCHOOL BUS

SCHOOL

Answer in the back.

Mimmy

Lorry

Kathy

Tim and Tammy

Tracy

These are photos of
Hello Kitty's friends.

Tippy

Fifi

Jody

You are Hello Kitty's friend too. Draw a picture of yourself.

NAME: _____

Fifi sits behind Hello Kitty at school.

Can you spot 10 differences between this page and the one before it?

Answers in the back.

Hello Kitty School Code

Hello Kitty wrote a note for you in secret code. Can you read the message? Use the Code Key below.

Code Key:

flower = S   book = u   apple = N   X = d

scissors = a   pencils = i   paintbrush = g   eraser = e

star = r   glasses = f

Secret Message:

star, eraser, scissors, X, pencils, apple, paintbrush !

pencils, flower, glasses, book, apple

Answer in the back.

Can you do these math problems?

$7 + 8 =$ $8 - 7 =$ $9 - 7 =$

$9 + 9 =$ $6 - 2 =$ $9 - 4 =$

$6 + 7 =$

$3 + 8 =$

$9 + 4 =$

Hello Kitty's art class is in the morning.

Draw a cute picture!

Art Supply Crossword Puzzle

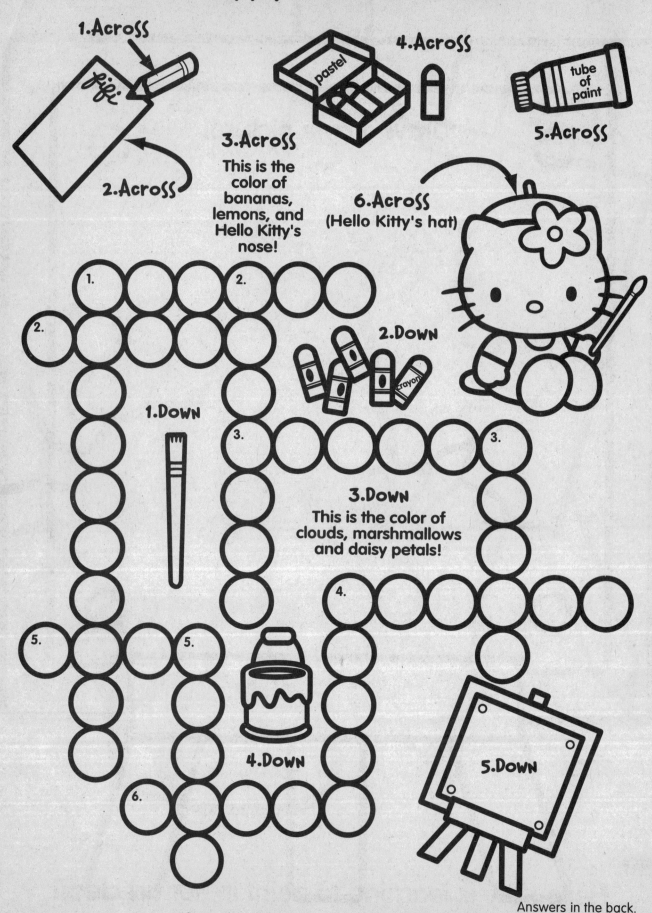

1.Across

2.Across

3.Across
This is the color of bananas, lemons, and Hello Kitty's nose!

4.Across

5.Across

6.Across
(Hello Kitty's hat)

pastel

tube of paint

1.Down

2.Down

3.Down
This is the color of clouds, marshmallows and daisy petals!

4.Down

5.Down

Answers in the back.

Hello Kitty is learning to paint in her art class!

Recess!

Pogo Race!

Can you figure out which path Hello Kitty, Tracy, and Kathy bounced on each of their pogo sticks?

Super Market

After school, Hello Kitty rides her bicycle to the supermarket.

Unscramble the List

What did Hello Kitty buy at the store?
Unscramble the words on her grocery list to find out!

Grocery List

ikml   _ _ _ _

rnaoeg iecuj   _ _ _ _ _ _ _ _ _ _

radeb   _ _ _ _ _

paleps   _ _ _ _ _ _

rocrats   _ _ _ _ _ _ _

bristwerasre   _ _ _ _ _ _ _ _ _ _ _

rgpase   _ _ _ _ _ _

Answers in the back.

Fresh Baked

2.5 6

Fresh baked cookies from the bakery are delicious.

Who Is Hiding?

Hello Kitty is waiting at the cafe for one of her friends.
Color in the spaces using the special color code
at the bottom of the page to find out who it is!

★ = pink   ✳ = light pink   ➰ = yellow
● = red   ♥ = blue   ■ = brown   ▲ = black

Hello Kitty wants to pick out a new dress.

Be Hello Kitty's Fashion Stylist!

Hello Kitty just bought some new clothes. Help her pick out a new hair accessory and a new purse to match each of her new outfits. Start at each Kitty and trace the way to the hair accessory and purse you think she should buy.

Hello Kitty loves to shop at all her favorite stores.

Find the Pair

Hello Kitty would like to buy some shoes...but they are all mixed up! Help her find the ONE pair of matching shoes by drawing a line from one shoe to the other. Look carefully! The shoes have to be an EXACT match.

Answers in the back.

Hello Kitty is looking
for some party shoes.

The flower shop always has lovely things!

Flower Bouquet

Help Hello Kitty finish picking out flowers to put in the bouquet she is going to give Mama. First, connect the dots and then color in the pretty picture.

Flower Find!
Can you find the 11 flowers that are hidden in the picture? Circle the flowers as you find them.

Look at all the pretty flowers Hello Kitty planted!

Mr. Policeman directs traffic in Hello Kitty's neighborhood.

Twin Policemen!

Can you spot the twins? Which two policemen are exactly the same?

Answers in the back.

There is a fire station in Hello Kitty's neighborhood.

Fight the Fire!

Help Hello Kitty and her fire fighting friends put out the fire. Find the way from the fire hydrant to the flames.

Answers in the back.

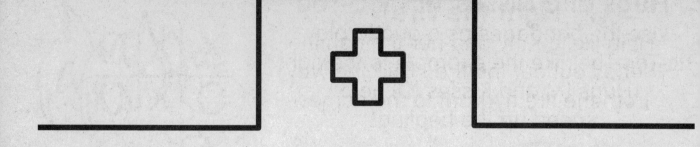

Hospital

Hello Kitty gets a check-up at the hospital.

Hugs and Kisses Tic-Tac-Toe

Use the bandages as a grid to play
Tic-Tac-Toe, like the example to the right.
Hugs (X) and Kisses (O) help
speed up the healing!

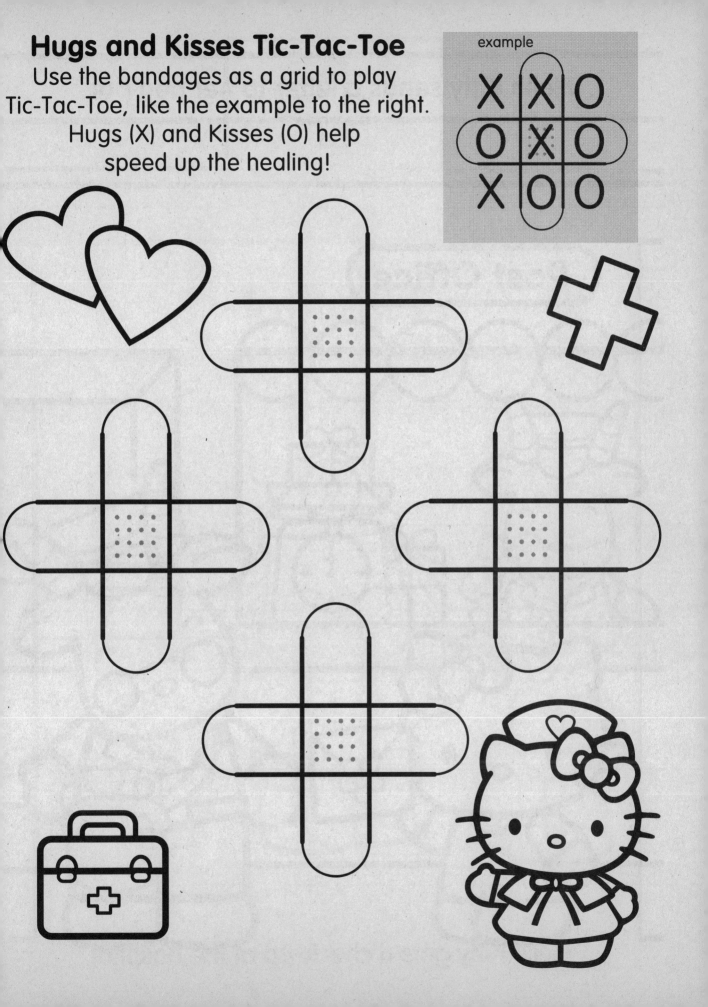

Hello Kitty sends a letter to her pen pal.

Connect the dots to see who has a special delivery!

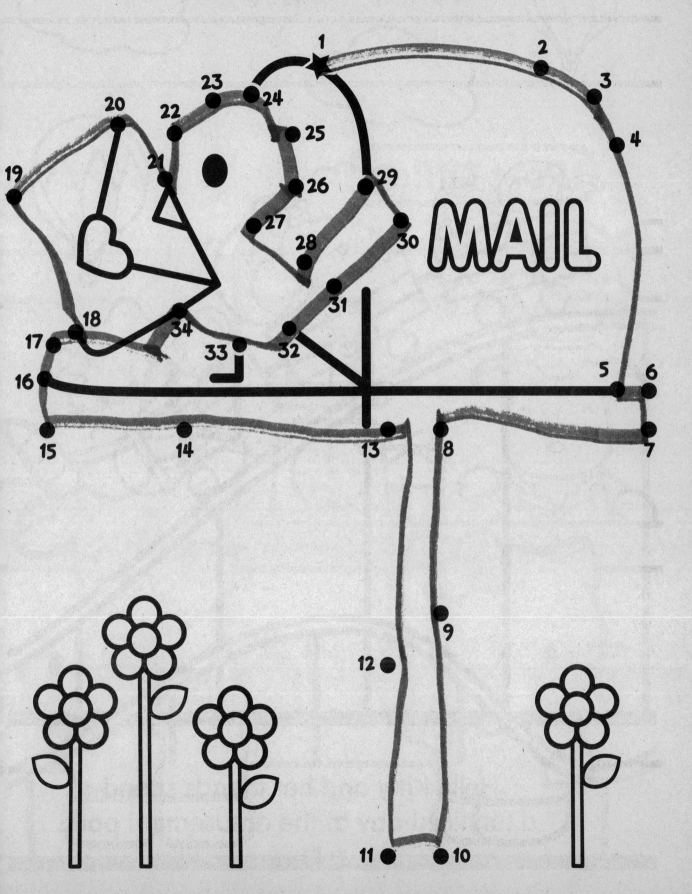

Hello Kitty and her friends spend
a fun filled day at the amusement park.

COTTON
CANDY

Hello Kitty gets a make-over at the beauty parlor.

Make-Over Time!

What does Hello Kitty feel like after she gets a makeover?
Using the clues at the bottom of the page, fill in the blanks.
The answer will be revealed in the rectangle.

1. _ _ _ _ _ _ _ _

2. _ _ _ _ _ _ _ _ _

3. _ _ _ _ _ _ _

4. _ _ _ _ _ _ _ _ _

5. _ _ _ _ _ _

6. _ _ _ _ _ _

7. _ _ _ _ _ _ _ _

8. _ _ _ _ _

1. This is what Hello Kitty washes her hair with
2. The place where Hello Kitty gets a makeover
3. Hello Kitty makes her fingernails pretty with this
4. This makes hair smooth and silky
5. Hello Kitty puts  in her hair to make it _____.
6. This smells pretty
7. These cut hair at the beauty parlor
8. Used to get tangles out of hair

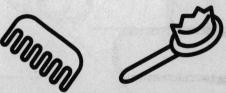

A make-over makes Hello Kitty feel like a _____.

Answers in the back.

Mimmy, Fifi, Kathy and Hello Kitty

practice ballet in front of a mirror.

Hello Kitty plays the piano
while her friends sing in choir class.

Making pretty music is fun!

Hello Kitty loves to learn about the history of art.

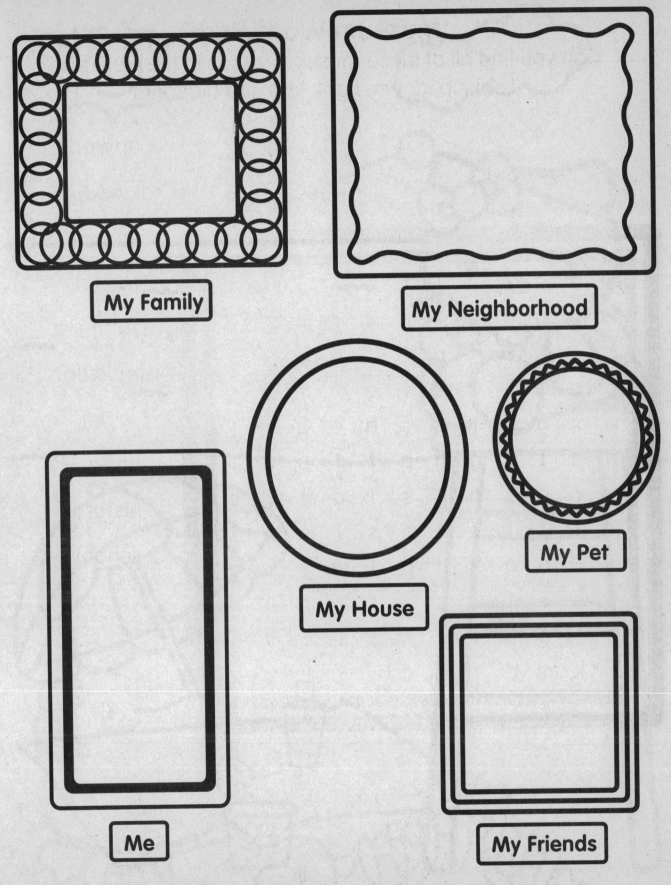

My Family

My Neighborhood

My House

My Pet

Me

My Friends

**Draw some pretty pictures
to hang on the wall of the art museum.**

Hello Kitty and friends go
to the beach on the weekend.

Fifi and Kathy wear sunscreen lotion.

There are a lot of fun things
to do at the beach!

Surf's Up!

Can you help Hello Kitty find her way back to the beach?

End

Start ↑

Answer in the back.

Hello Kitty and her friends like to play

Everyone takes a turn.

They also like to have picnics

and ride bikes in the park too.

There are so many cute animals at the zoo!

Petting animals at the zoo is always exciting!

Hide and Seek

The animals are playing hide and seek in Hello Kitty's neighborhood. Can you help her find 2 sheep, 3 bunnies, and 5 baby chicks?

Hello Kitty likes to visit Farmer Brown's farm.

Connect the dots to see what
Hello Kitty is doing on the farm!

Hello Kitty's friends like visiting
the library to check out books.

Reading is fun, but remember
to be quiet in the library!

It is a delight to eat
at a nice restaurant.

Help the waiter find his way to Hello Kitty's table.

Answer in the back.

Children's Matinee

Tickets

Hello Kitty's neighborhood has a movie theater.

Draw a scene from your favorite movie on the movie screen!

Can you figure out which route Hello Kitty flew in her airplane?

The train finally came!

Hello Kitty's neighborhood has fun parades on special days!

✿ Answers ✿

Good Morning!

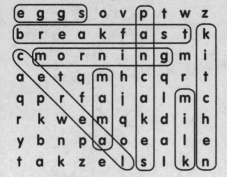

```
e g g s o v p t w z
b r e a k f a s t k i
c m o r n i n g m i t
a e t q m h c q r c
q p r f a j l d h
r k w e m q k d i e
y b n p a o e a l k
t a k z e l s l k n
```

Hello Kitty School Code
Reading is fun!

Bus Maze

Spot the Differences

1. Missing cloud
2. Flower on the slide
3. Missing bird outside
4. Different time on the clock
5. Fifi's backpack
6. Kitty's backpack
7. The shape of Kitty's paper
8. Fifi's scissors
9. The picture on Fifi's paper
10. Fifi's flower bow

Art Supply Crossword

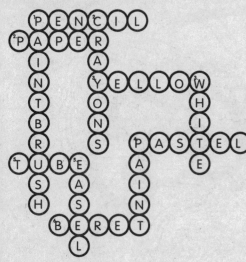

Unscramble the List

ikml <u>milk</u>

rnaoeg iecuj <u>orange juice</u>

radeb <u>bread</u>

paleps <u>apples</u>

rocrats <u>carrots</u>

bristwerasre <u>strawberries</u>

rgpase <u>grapes</u>

Bakery Word Find

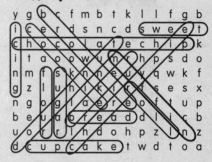

```
y g b c f m b t k l l f g b
i c e r d s n c d s w e e t
c h o c o l a t e c h i p k
i t a o o w u r h p s d o
n m f s k n n e u q w k f
g z l u h l r s e s x
n g o g l a e r e o f t u p
b e u a b r e a d d l c b
u o r r l h d o h p z l n z
d c u p c a k e t w d t o a
```

Find the Pair

Twin Policemen!

1.

5.

Fight the Fire!

🌸 Answers 🌸

Make-Over Time!

1. s h a m p o o
2. b e a u t y   p a r l o r
3. n a i l   p o l i s h
4. c o n d i t i o n e r
5. c u r l e r s
6. p e r f u m e
7. s c i s s o r s
8. b r u s h

A makeover makes Hello Kitty feel like a p r i n c e s s.

Museum Word Find

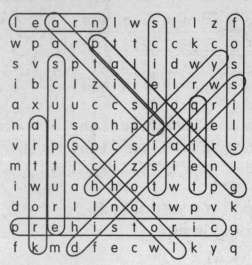

l	e	a	r	n	l	w	s	l	l	z	f
w	p	a	r	p	t	t	c	c	k	c	o
s	v	s	p	t	a	l	i	d	w	y	s
i	b	c	l	z	i	i	e	l	r	w	s
a	x	u	u	c	c	s	n	o	q	r	i
n	a	l	s	o	h	p	t	t	u	e	l
v	r	p	s	p	c	s	i	a	i	r	s
m	t	t	l	c	i	z	s	i	e	n	l
i	w	u	a	h	h	o	t	w	t	p	g
d	o	r	l	l	n	o	t	w	p	v	k
p	r	e	h	i	s	t	o	r	i	c	g
f	k	m	d	f	e	c	w	l	k	y	q

Surf's up!

Waiter Maze

Movie Time Fun

z	s	e	f	w	i	s	c	s	i	m	h
h	z	c	i	e	b	t	e	o	i	a	r
d	i	u	p	s	f	a	e	u	t	p	a
t	a	z	o	o	l	r	n	n	w	h	c
i	o	n	p	u	t	f	i	d	r	c	t
c	h	o	c	o	l	a	t	e	b	a	r
k	m	q	o	i	l	s	a	f	n	n	e
e	o	m	r	e	n	o	m	f	t	d	s
t	v	d	n	f	c	g	d	e	i	y	s
s	i	n	g	i	n	g	p	c	i	q	o
c	e	i	s	t	h	e	a	t	e	r	d
l	a	u	g	h	d	l	a	s	p	q	a